HERCULES
AND THE
GOLDEN APPLES

retold by Della Rowland
illustrated by Donna Perrone

McGraw-Hill
School Division

New York   Farmington

A Greek myth tells that long ago, in the most Western part of the world known to the Greeks, was the ancient Garden of the Hesperides. There, on the highest hilltop, grew a magical tree with golden branches and golden leaves, from whose boughs hung beautiful golden apples.

The tree had been a wedding gift to a goddess named Hera, and she did not want anyone to touch her precious tree. Many brave adventurers dreamed of picking the golden fruit, but none had ever succeeded, and there were good reasons why.

First, only the gods knew where the Garden was, and no mortal could force a god to divulge such information. Second, they made sure the tree was well guarded. Coiled around its trunk was a ferocious dragon with a hundred fire-breathing heads that never slept, and standing guard with the dragon were four fearless warriors, the Daughters of the West.

So, as it was, even if a clever mortal found the Garden by tricking a god or goddess who knew its location, he or she would never get close enough to the tree to pick a single apple without becoming dinner for a hundred hungry heads!

Nevertheless, one mighty hero did accomplish this feat. That hero was Hercules, and this is the story of how Hercules obtained the golden apples.

Hercules was a brave hero, who was determined to prove that he was the strongest man in the world. Even as an infant he had amazing strength and was completely fearless. Yet Hercules had enemies among the gods. One god sent two huge and hideous snakes to crawl into his crib. To the amazement of his terrified parents, the infant Hercules grabbed a snake in each hand and crushed them. Later, when he was only eighteen, he killed a fierce lion. From then on, he always wore the lion skin.

Unfortunately, Hercules was not as smart as he was strong, because he was ruled by his heart and not his head, and he sometimes did terrible things without thinking and was sorry for them later. Although Hercules always tried to make up for his wrongdoing and was glad to accept severe punishment, he never seemed to learn from his mistakes, even as an adult.

Finally the gods themselves decided that they had to punish Hercules, so they decreed that he had to complete twelve impossible tasks devised by his cousin, King Eurystheus. If he failed any one of them, he would be sentenced to die a horrible death.

These tasks Eurytheus assigned him are known as "the twelve labors of Hercules". They included killing monsters, such as the twelve-headed Hydra, and capturing magical animals, such as the cattle of Geryon. No typical mortal could have completed a single one of these tasks, but the twelfth labor was by far the most difficult: to bring Eurystheus three golden apples from the Garden of the Hesperides.

Because of his extraordinary strength, Hercules had total confidence in his ability to accomplish any impossible feat. He had already completed eleven of the labors, so fearlessly he set out to find the tree which grew the golden apples. First he had to find someone who knew where the Garden was. He wandered about the country asking everyone he met, but no one could tell him. At last his travels led him to a beautiful, wide river, where he rested.

While he was sitting on the bank, Hercules noticed five Water Maidens playing in the water and twining fragrant blossoms into flower chains. "Pretty Maidens," he called out, "can you tell me where I can find the Garden of the Hesperides?"

The Water Maidens dropped their flowers and looked at each other in dismay. "Why has my question caused so much confusion?" Hercules laughed.

"We cannot understand why you would want to find this Garden," answered a maiden sadly.

"Surely you know that many strong young men like you have come seeking the golden apples," said another. "Not one of them has ever returned."

"And neither will you," said a third.

"A horrible dragon guards the tree," confided the fourth.

"And the Four Daughters of the West," added the fifth.

"I am Hercules, the strongest man in the world—I am not afraid of anything," he told them. Then he began telling the Water Maidens one story after another about his amazing feats of strength. It took him three days to describe all the monsters he had conquered and the impossible tasks he had performed. When he had finished, the maidens whispered among themselves, and then they addressed Hercules.

"After hearing your stories, we believe you are the strongest man in the world," said the first maiden. "You may indeed be the one who finally picks the golden apples, so we will help you in your quest."

"Nereus, the Old Man of the Sea, knows where the Garden of the Hesperides is," said the second.

"Follow this river—it will lead you to the sea where he lives," advised the third.

"We saw him sleeping on a rock a few days ago," said the fourth. "He likes to take long naps, so he is probably still there."

The fifth warned: "Remember this—hold on tight to Nereus until he tells you what you want to know—no matter what happens."

Hercules thanked the Water Maidens for their help and began walking along the river. After several days, he reached the sea where, sure enough, he found Nereus still asleep on a long, flat rock. His hair and beard were green seaweed and his skin was covered with silvery scales. Before he could awaken, Hercules seized him in his powerful hands.

"Let me go!" cried Nereus, kicking and struggling.

"Not until you tell me what I wish to know," said Hercules.

Hoping to slither out of the stranger's grip, Nereus changed into a slippery fish, then a wriggling eel. Nevertheless, Hercules held on tight, so the old man became a three-headed dog that snarled and snapped at Hercules' hands. When that failed to cause Hercules to drop him, Nereus became a bird which wildly flapped its scaly wings at Hercules' head. Still, Hercules held on even tighter.

Then Nereus changed into a stream and nearly slipped through Hercules' fingers, but somehow Hercules managed to keep his grip. At last, Nereus gave up his struggle and returned to his original form. "Who are you and what do you want?" he demanded.

"I am Hercules, and I will keep you in hand until you tell me where I can find the Garden of the Hesperides. Then I will let you go."

When Nereus heard the name Hercules, he knew it was of no use to struggle. "The garden is on an island near Africa," he replied. "You will never pick the apples, however, for the only one who can do that is Atlas, the strongest man in the world."

"Hah!" shouted Hercules, squeezing Nereus practically to the point of crushing him. "I am the strongest man in the world."

Nereus gasped. "Atlas is so strong he holds up the sky on his shoulders."

Hercules stubbornly stuck out his chin and boasted, "I am not afraid of Atlas. Tell me where I can find him."

"You will find Atlas in Africa, too," Nereus told him. "Look for the mountains, and there he will be." Hearing this, Hercules let go of Nereus, who immediately dove into the sea and swam away as fast as he could.

Hercules' journey to Africa took fourteen days, most of it on foot. Soon Hercules came upon a huge lodge. "Perhaps the owner can tell me where the mountains are, and how to find Atlas," he thought.

Before Hercules had reached the door, a giant came striding out of the lodge and stood right before him. The giant was twice his size, with arms the size of tree trunks and thighs as big around as boulders. "Are you Atlas?" Hercules asked fearlessly.

The giant roared, "I am Antaeus, son of Terra the Earth goddess, and the strongest man in the world. If you wish to enter my country, you must wrestle me first."

"Gladly!" cried Hercules, for this was the thing he loved to do best. "We shall see who is the strongest man in the world."

The two wrestled for hours. Again and again, Hercules threw the giant to the ground, but each time Antaeus struck the ground, he jumped up ten times stronger than ever. Hercules began to think he had met his match. Then Hercules guessed the secret to the giant's strength: it was the very ground itself. Antaeus said that he was the son of Terra, the Earth goddess. Each time the giant touched the ground, Terra's strength flowed from the earth into her son. Now Hercules knew what to do.

One last time Antaeus leapt up from the ground and sprang at Hercules. This time Hercules caught him in midair and held him high. The giant struggled to get out of Hercules' grip and back onto the ground, but the longer Hercules held him aloft the weaker he became. Terra could no longer help her son, and Antaeus was defeated.

With no one to stand in his way, Hercules set out again to find Atlas. At last he came upon a lovely valley that ran through a chain of high, craggy mountains. Walking through this valley, he suddenly found himself standing before two massive legs.

The legs were almost as tall as the mountains themselves, with each one as thick as fifty tree trunks bound together, and each sandal on each gigantic foot was as big as a house. Looking up to the clouds, Hercules saw the rest of the giant towering high above him.

The giant was taller than the mountains that surrounded him. The clouds swirled around his head and clung to his face like a white beard. His shoulders were as wide as the sky, and, indeed, that is just what rested on them. Hercules did not have to ask his name—he had found Atlas!

When the clouds parted, Hercules could see Atlas' face. It was lined with fatigue—and no wonder. He had stood in this spot so long holding up the sky that a forest of mighty oak trees had sprung up between his toes.

Hercules cupped his hands and called up as loudly as he could, "Atlas, can you hear me?"

"Who is that down there with such a mighty voice?" inquired Atlas, straining to see Hercules across the great distance.

"I am Hercules and I've come to ask your assistance. I have been commanded to fetch three golden apples from the tree in the Garden of the Hesperides. Is it true that only you can pluck these golden apples?"

"It is true—I cannot help you, because to do so I would have to let go of the sky," replied Atlas. "If I do that the sky will fall down on Earth and all life on it will be destroyed."

"I am the strongest man in the world," boasted Hercules. "I can hold up the sky for you if you will pick the apples for me."

Atlas chuckled and asked, "Are you sure you are strong enough to do such a thing?"

Hercules' pride swelled at the thought of how famous he would be if it were known that he had held up the sky. Then there would truly be no doubt that he was the strongest man in the world—except for gigantic Atlas himself. "Of course I can," he answered boldly, "you'll see."

Hercules then climbed the high mountain until his shoulders were at the level of the sky, and Atlas gently shifted the sky onto his shoulders. Hercules groaned—the sky was far heavier than he had imagined.

Atlas laughed at his discomfort. "I thought you were the strongest man in the world. Now you see what I have endured for centuries." He stretched his arms. "Ahh, it feels good to stretch and stand up straight!"

"How far away is this garden?" asked Hercules.

"A long trek for you," responded Atlas, "but, for me, it is just a few steps across the sea."

"Then hurry back," Hercules begged, "the sky is very heavy."

Atlas set off with great strides for the West and the Garden of the Hesperides. With his first stride he was half way across Africa. His next stride put his foot at the edge of the sea. One more step and he was in middle of the sea up to his waist in water. Then he disappeared from sight.

Once he could no longer see Atlas, Hercules began to worry. What if Atlas should drown or be eaten by the dragon with a hundred heads? Could he really hold up the sky for centuries, as Atlas had? What if he dropped the sky—how ashamed then he would be!

To his great joy, it was only a short time later that Hercules saw Atlas striding back. When the giant opened his huge hand, in it lay the three golden apples, and Hercules gasped at their beauty. As big as pumpkins, they were the color of pure honey, and they shone like the sun.

"I think I shall be your messenger to King Eurystheus," declared Atlas. "I will take the apples back for you and let you hold up the sky for a while longer."

For once Hercules was as clever as he was strong. "Very well," he shouted up to the giant, "but it is cold on this mountain top, Atlas, and I'm afraid I might freeze at night when the sun goes down. Besides, the sky is scraping my shoulders. Before you go, allow me to put my lion skin over my shoulders to cushion the sky and keep me warm."

"That is a fair request," said Atlas. So he placed the apples on the ground and shouldered the sky once more.

As soon as Hercules threw his lion skin over his shoulders Atlas bent down to give him back the sky, but Hercules did not take it. Instead, he put the golden apples in his bag and quickly set off down the mountain.

"Come back!" Atlas roared angrily. "Come back!" Hercules could hear Atlas all the way across Africa. Each time the giant shouted to him, it was like thunder rolling from the mountain tops.

When Hercules presented Eurystheus with the three golden apples, the King could not believe that Hercules had accomplished this feat. Eurystheus praised Hercules and ordered a feast be set out, a meal so rich and grand that no one ever forgot it.

Now that his twelve labors were complete, the gods forgave Hercules for his past mistakes. Still, his life was never a quiet one. Hercules remained a hero and had amazing adventures for the rest of his life, but those are tales for another time!